Look at th

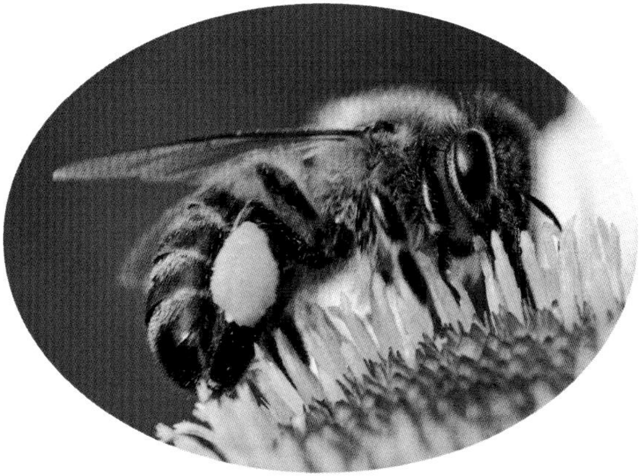

by Jay Dale

Look at the bee.

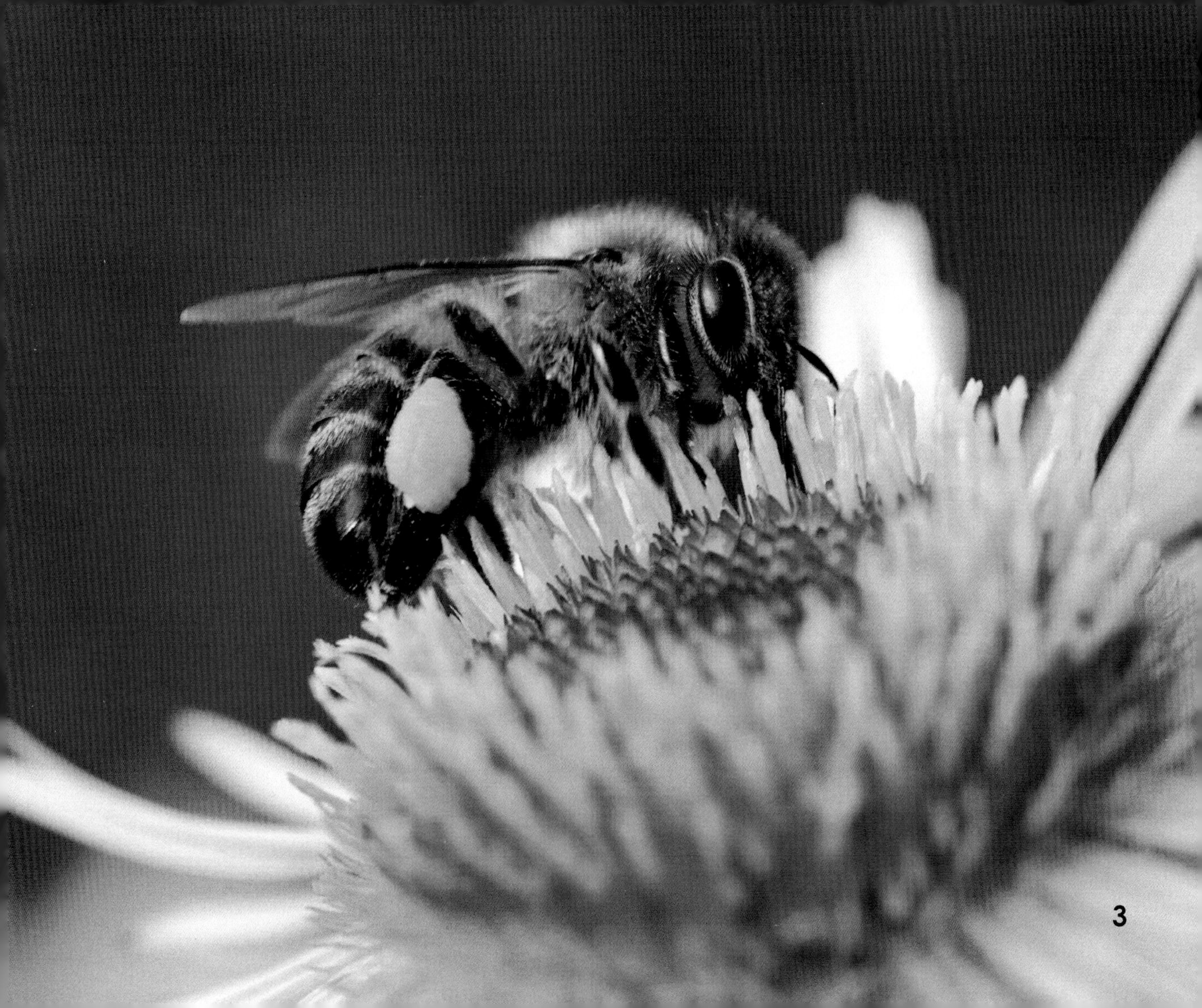

Look at the caterpillar.

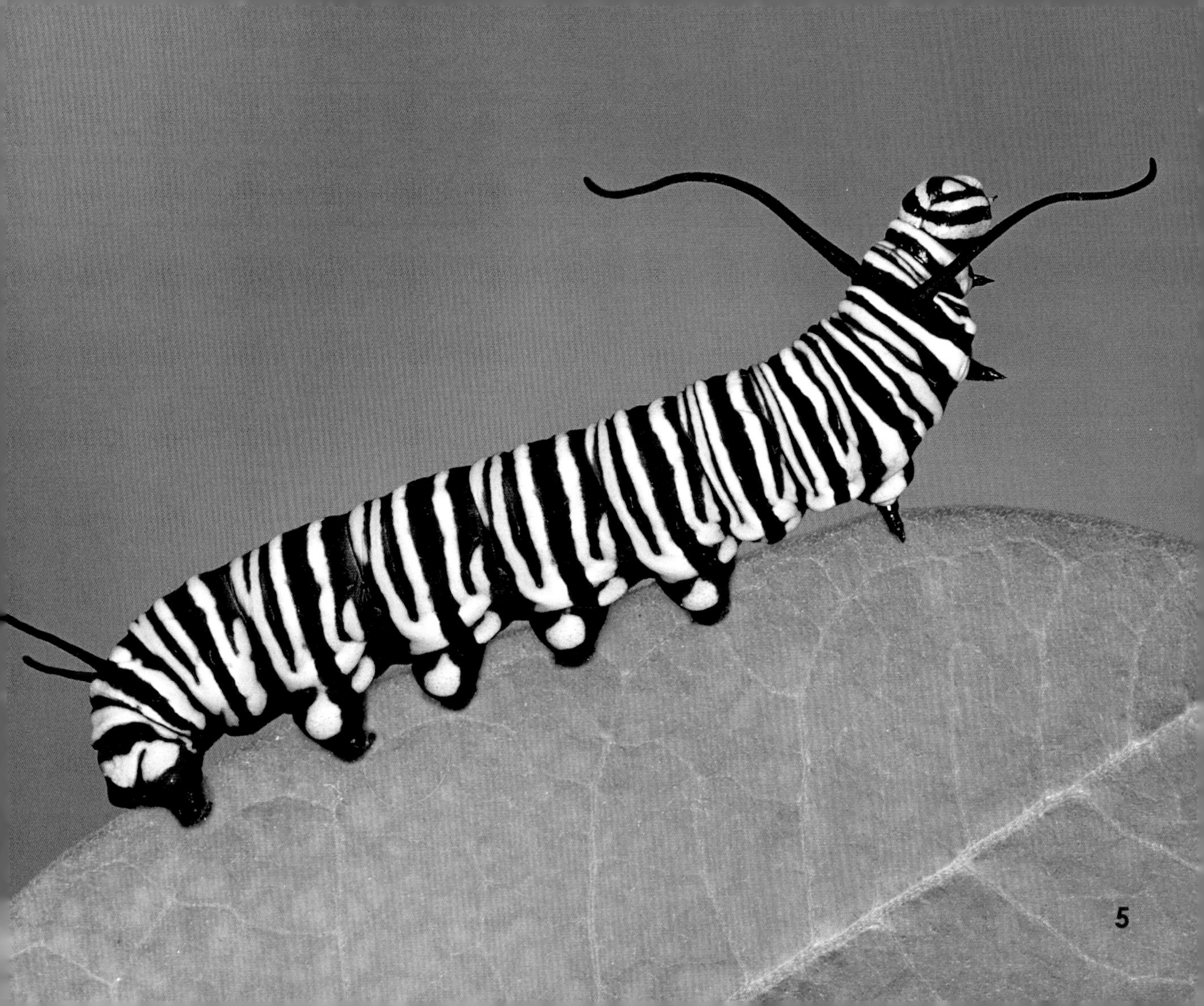

Look at the butterfly.

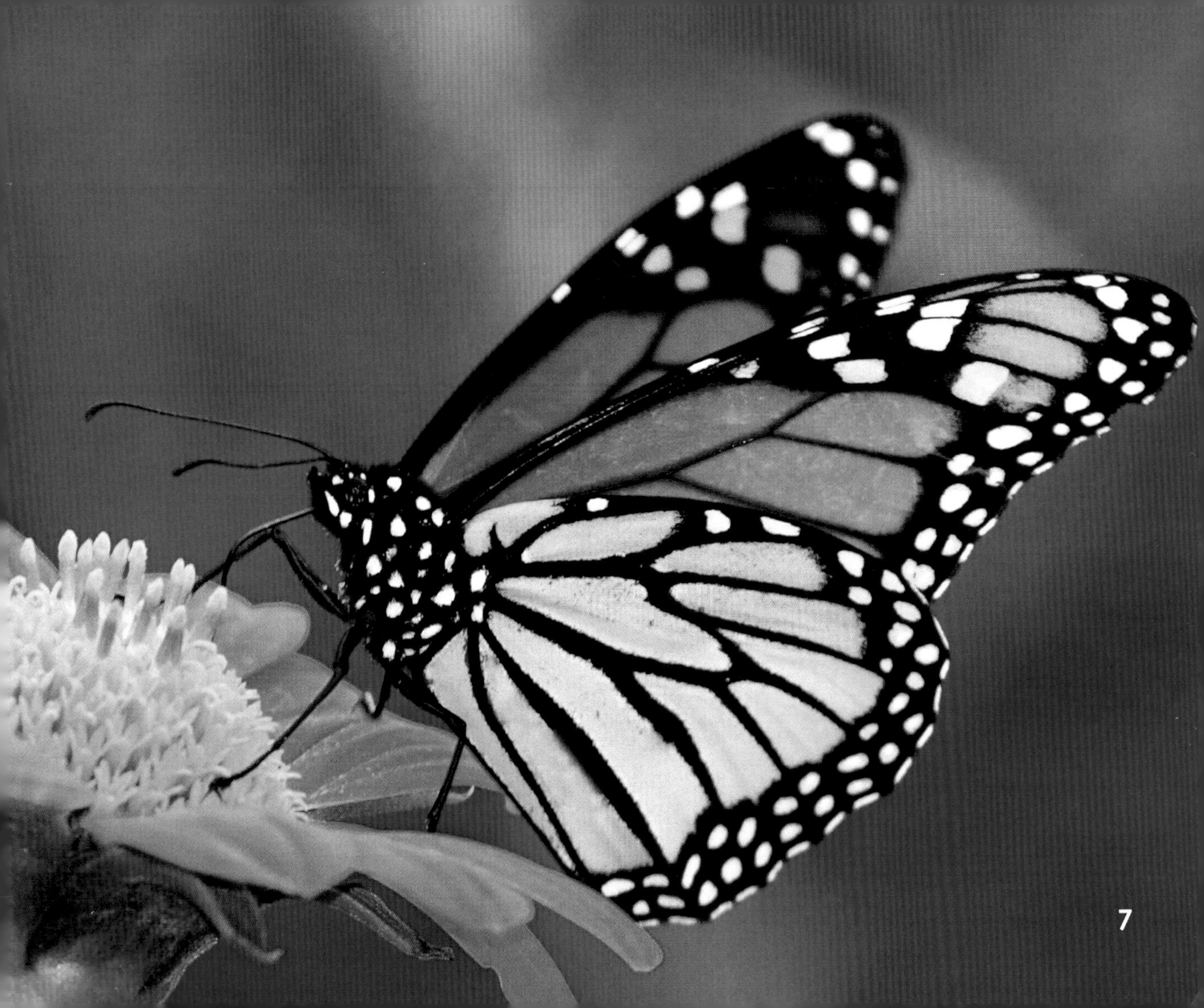

Look at the ladybird.

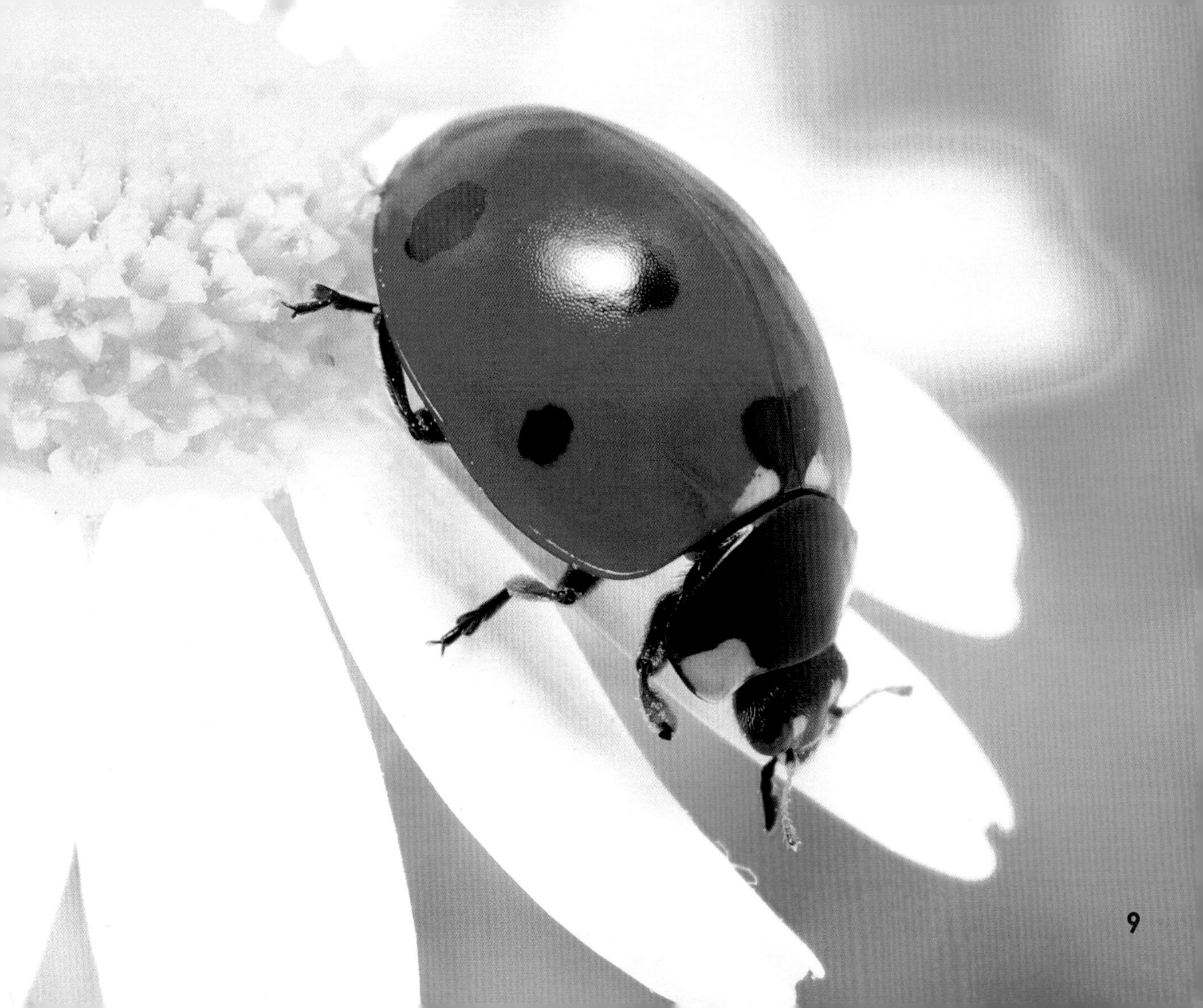

Look at the ant.

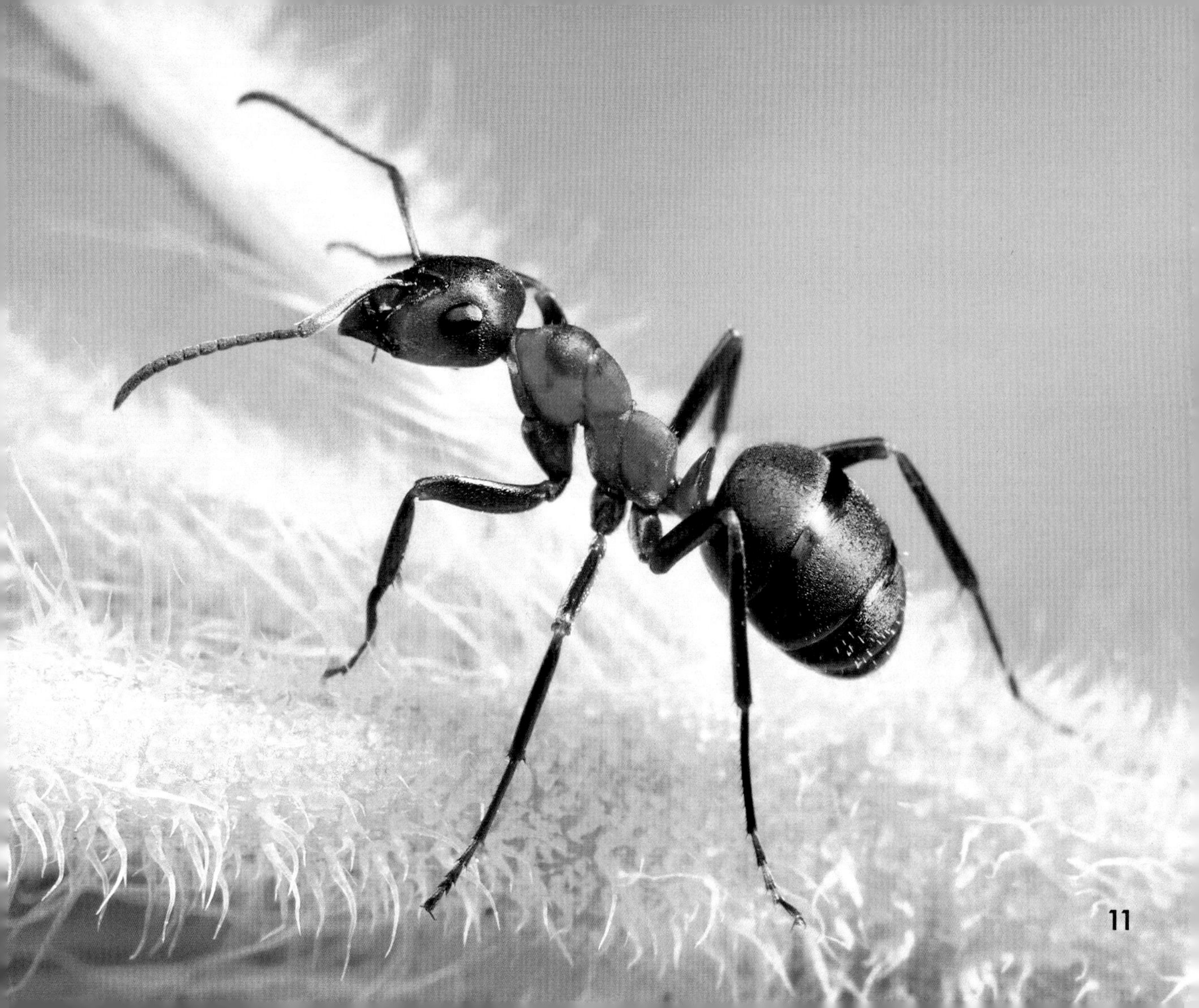

Look at the spider.

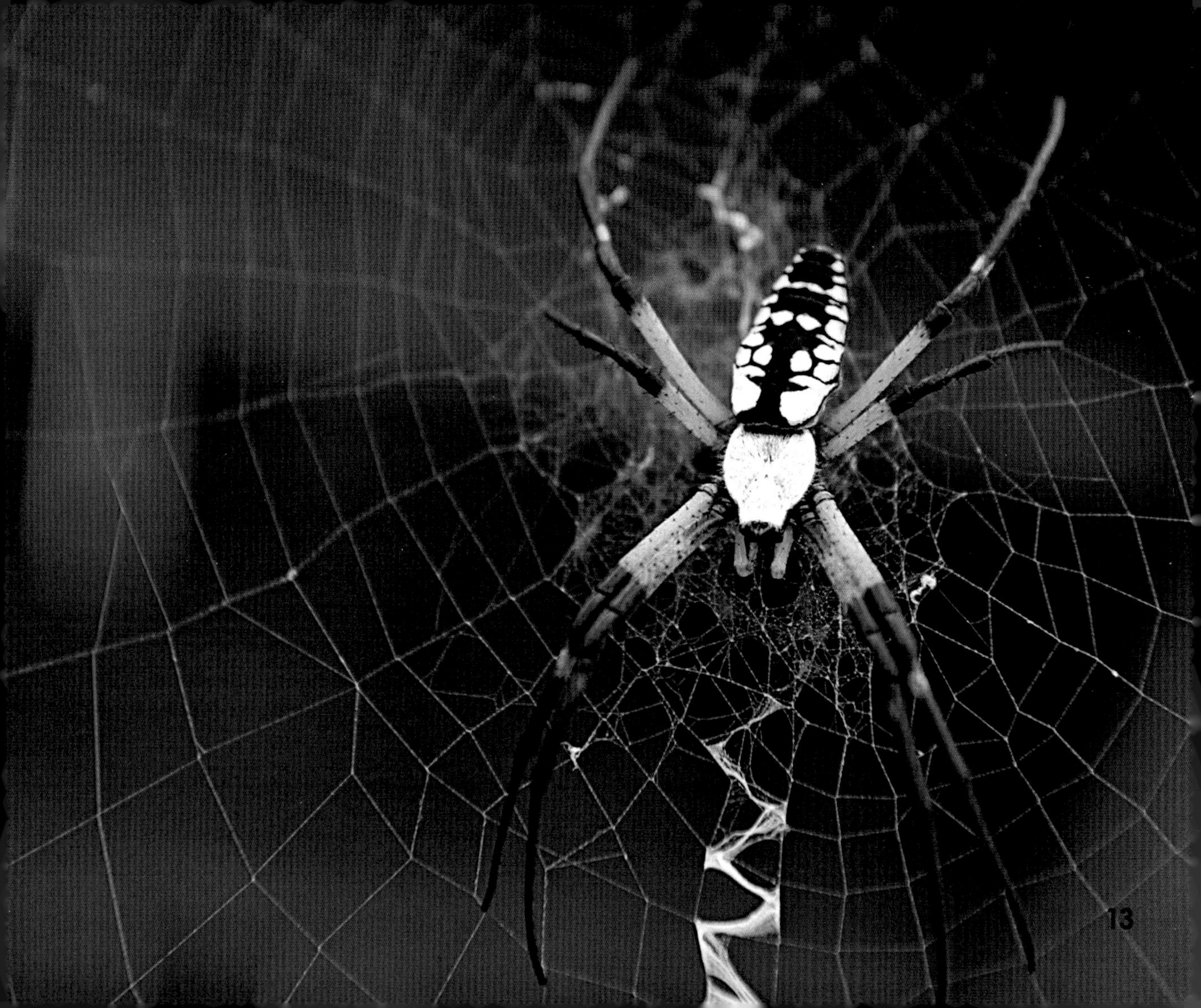

Look at the worm.

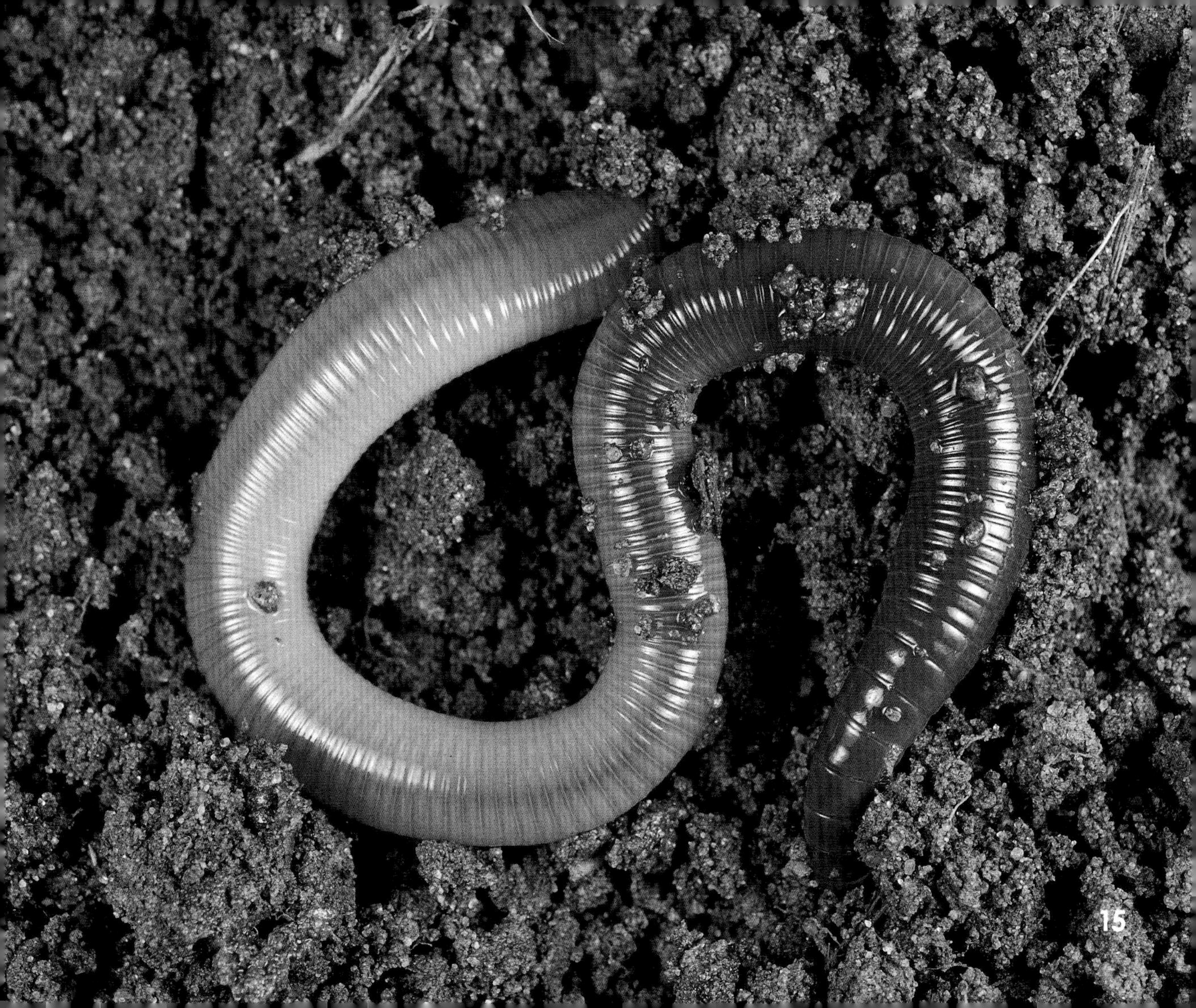

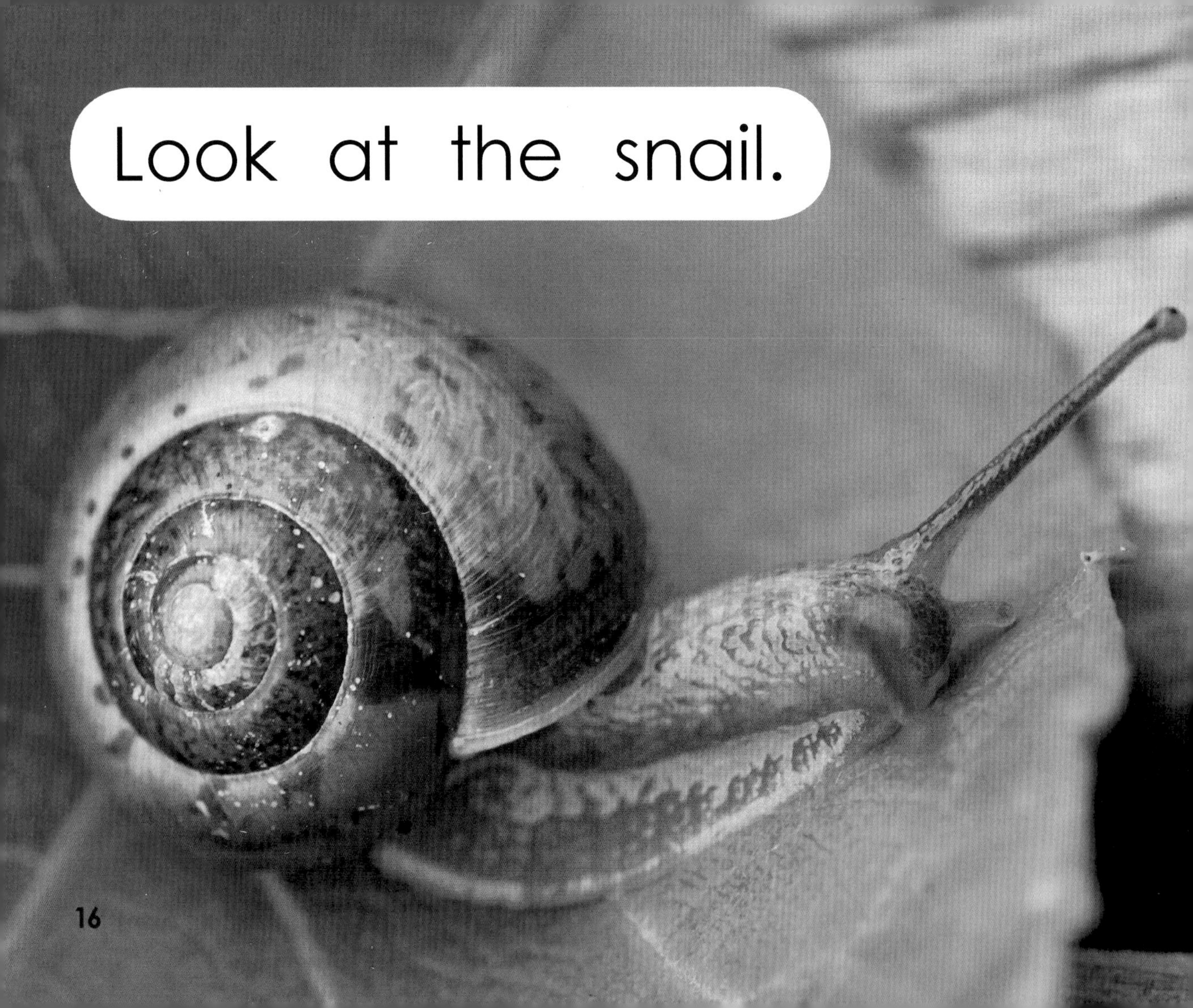

Look at the snail.